Edited by
Lori Jacobs Frischknecht

Book Design by
Melissa Jepsen Johns

Published by
The Living Scriptures, Inc.
P.O. Box 3952
Ogden, UT 84409

ISBN # 1-56473-157-X

First Printing, 1992

Printed in the United States of America

AMMON, MISSIONARY TO THE LAMANITES

LAURIE BONNELL STEPHENS

THE LIVING SCRIPTURES®

Ogden, Utah

Mosiah was the king of the Nephites. He and his four sons, Ammon, Aaron, Omner and Himni lived in the land of Zarahemla. Mosiah was a righteous king, and he always obeyed the commandments of God. **(see Mosiah 25:19; Mosiah 27:34-36)**

Ammon, Aaron, Omner and Himni were very righteous too. They were great missionaries and loved to preach the gospel to other people. The sons of Mosiah spent most of their time traveling all over the land teaching the Nephites about Jesus Christ.

One day King Mosiah called his four sons together. Mosiah was getting old, and he wanted one of his sons to take his place as king of the Nephites. (Mosiah 28:1-10; 27:34-37; Alma 17:2-3; 6)

But when Mosiah asked his sons if one of them would become the new king, they all refused. King Mosiah's sons did not want to be king. They wanted to go on other missions, so they could teach the gospel.

The sons of Mosiah wanted to go to the land of the Lamanites. They wanted to teach the Lamanites about Jesus Christ.

(Mosiah 28:1-5; 10)

6

This worried King Mosiah. The Lamanites did not like the Nephites. King Mosiah was afraid that his sons would be killed, if he let them go to the land of the Lamanites.

(see Mosiah 28:5-6)

King Mosiah
prayed to the
Lord. He asked the
Lord if he should
let his sons go
teach the gospel
to the Lamanites.

(Mosiah 28:6-7)

9

The Lord spoke to King Mosiah. He told Mosiah not to worry. The Lord promised to protect the sons of Mosiah from danger, while they were on their missions. He told Mosiah that his sons would bring many Lamanites into the church, if Mosiah would let them go. **(Mosiah 28:7)**

After he had prayed, King Mosiah was not worried. He agreed to let his sons go preach the gospel to the Lamanites.

(Mosiah 28:6-8)

11

Ammon, Aaron, Omner and Himni were happy. They left home together to begin their missions.

When the sons of Mosiah reached the land of the Lamanites, they knelt down and prayed. They asked the Lord to help them find those Lamanites who would listen to the gospel. **(Mosiah 28:9; Alma 17:6-13; 18)**

After their prayer, the four brothers waved
goodbye. They all went in different directions,
so they could preach the gospel to as many
Lamanites as possible. **(Alma 17:13; 17)**

Ammon traveled alone to the land of Ishmael.
When the Lamanites saw Ammon in their land,
they captured him and took him before the
Lamanite king,
Lamoni.

(Alma 17:19-21)

King Lamoni asked Ammon many questions. The Lamanites did not like Nephites to come into their land. King Lamoni wanted to know why Ammon was there.

Ammon was not frightened. When he told King Lamoni that he wanted to live with the Lamanites for awhile, Lamoni was pleased.

King Lamoni was so pleased, that he asked Ammon to marry one of his daughters.

But Ammon did not want to marry one of King Lamoni's daughters. Instead, Ammon told King Lamoni that he wanted to be his servant. **(Alma 17:20- 25)**

This made King Lamoni happy. Lamoni decided that Ammon should be one of the servants who watched over his flocks.

Ammon was glad to serve King Lamoni. He went with the other servants to watch over the king's flocks. **(Alma 17:25)**

One day as Ammon and the other servants were taking King Lamoni's flocks to water, wicked Lamanite robbers came and scattered the flocks in many directions. The robbers scattered the flocks, so they could steal them from the king. **(Alma 17:27; Alma 18:7)**

The Lamanite servants were frightened. The king's flocks had run away, and the servants did not know what to do. They knew that King Lamoni would have them killed for losing all his flocks. **(Alma 17:28-29)**

But Ammon was not frightened. He had faith in God. He knew that the Lord would help them find the king's flocks. Ammon told the other servants to help him look for the flocks and gather them together, so the king would not have the servants killed.

Ammon and King Lamoni's servants looked for the flocks. Quickly, they gathered them all together and brought them back to the water.

(Alma 17:28-32)

Once again the robbers came to scatter King Lamoni's flocks. Quickly Ammon commanded the king's servants to stand around the flocks, so they would not run away. Then Ammon went and stood against the thieves alone. **(Alma 17:33-34)**

The wicked Lamanites were not afraid of Ammon. They liked to scatter the king's flocks and wanted to kill Ammon for trying to stop them. They did not know that the Lord had promised to protect Ammon. **(Alma 17:34-35)**

Ammon was not afraid either. He knew the Lord would protect him. When the robbers would not stop trying to scatter the flocks, Ammon threw stones at them with his sling.

The Lord made Ammon strong. Ammon threw the stones so hard, that some of the thieves were killed. **(Alma 17:34-36)**

The robbers were angry at Ammon for killing their friends. They were so angry, that they tried to kill Ammon with stones. But the Lord protected Ammon. He would not let the thieves kill Ammon. **(Alma 17:35-37)**

The thieves became
more and more angry. When they could not kill Ammon
with stones, they tried to kill him with their clubs.
Ammon drew his sword to defend himself from the
wicked robbers. He used his sword to slay their leader.
Then Ammon cut off the arms of the robbers who were
trying to
kill him
with their
clubs.

(Alma 17:36-38)

King Lamoni's servants were surprised at Ammon's strength. They were happy that Ammon had protected the king's flocks from the robbers. The servants ran to tell King Lamoni what had happened. When King Lamoni saw the arms of the wicked men and heard what Ammon had done, he was amazed. **(Alma 17:26-39; Alma 18:1-2)**

29

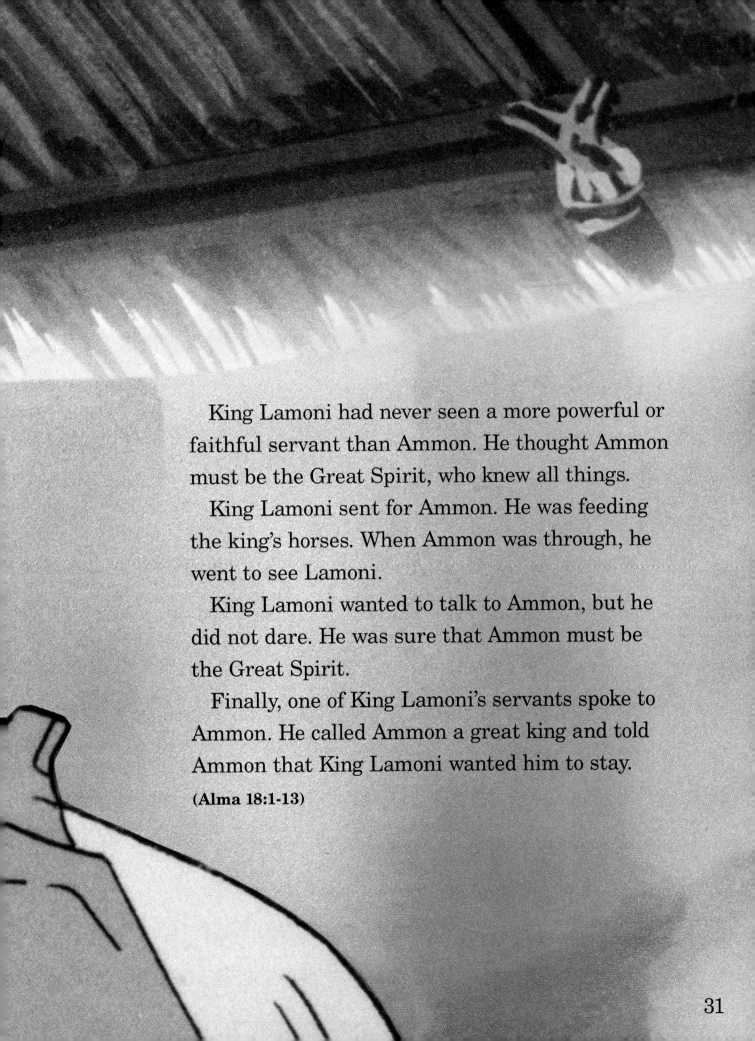

King Lamoni had never seen a more powerful or faithful servant than Ammon. He thought Ammon must be the Great Spirit, who knew all things.

King Lamoni sent for Ammon. He was feeding the king's horses. When Ammon was through, he went to see Lamoni.

King Lamoni wanted to talk to Ammon, but he did not dare. He was sure that Ammon must be the Great Spirit.

Finally, one of King Lamoni's servants spoke to Ammon. He called Ammon a great king and told Ammon that King Lamoni wanted him to stay.

(Alma 18:1-13)

31

Ammon asked King Lamoni what he wanted, but the king did not dare speak.

The Lord blessed Ammon. He helped Ammon know what King Lamoni was thinking.

King Lamoni was surprised when he found out that Ammon could read his thoughts. Lamoni asked Ammon if he was the Great Spirit. **(Alma 18:14-19)**

Ammon was not the Great Spirit. When he told King Lamoni that he was just a man, Lamoni wanted to know why Ammon had such power.

Ammon told Lamoni that he was a messenger sent from God. He taught King Lamoni the gospel of Jesus Christ. **(Alma 18:18-40)**

King Lamoni believed all of Ammon's words. He knew that the gospel was true and wanted to be forgiven of his sins.

King Lamoni prayed and begged the Lord to have mercy on him and his people. **(Alma 18:40-41)**

After King Lamoni finished praying, he fell to the ground. When Lamoni did not speak or move, his servants thought that he was dead. They carried King Lamoni in to the queen and laid him on his bed. **(Alma 18:42-43)**

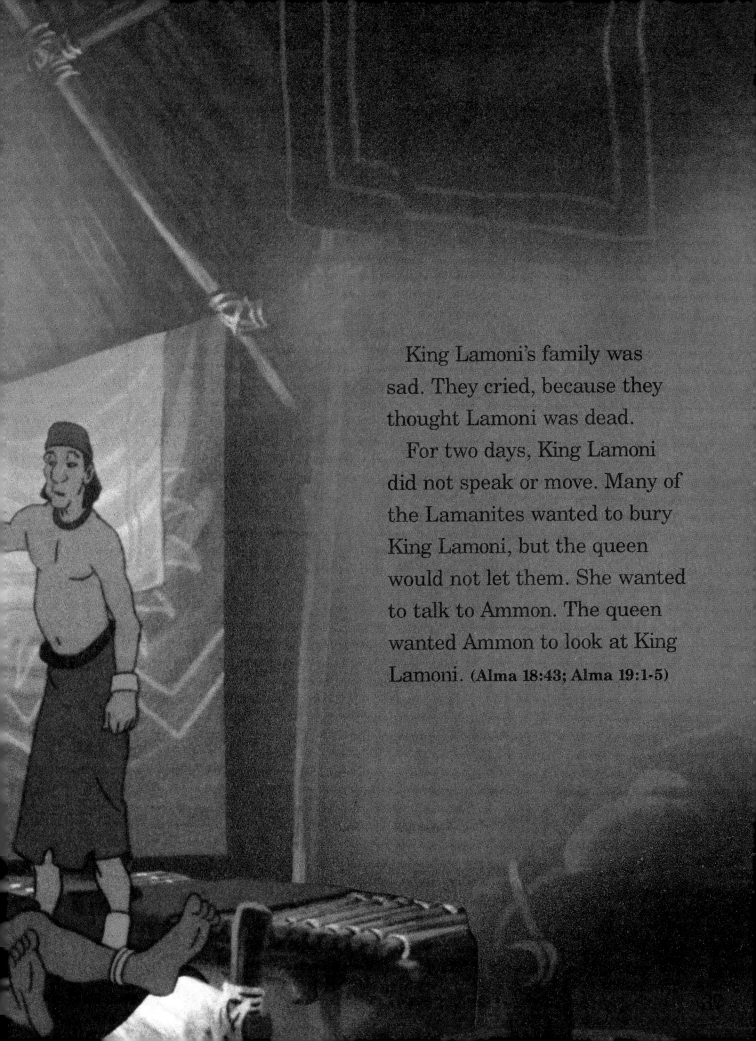

King Lamoni's family was
sad. They cried, because they
thought Lamoni was dead.

For two days, King Lamoni
did not speak or move. Many of
the Lamanites wanted to bury
King Lamoni, but the queen
would not let them. She wanted
to talk to Ammon. The queen
wanted Ammon to look at King
Lamoni. **(Alma 18:43; Alma 19:1-5)**

When Ammon looked at King Lamoni, he knew the king was not dead. Ammon knew that King Lamoni had been filled with the Spirit of God. He knew that Lamoni was gaining a testimony of the gospel, and that he would rise again.

(Alma 19:6-7)

Ammon promised the queen that King Lamoni
would rise again the next day.

The queen was happy. She believed Ammon
and had faith that King Lamoni was not dead.

(Alma 19:8-10)

The next day King Lamoni rose. He had seen the Lord, and his heart was filled with joy.

Once again, King Lamoni fell to the earth. This time the queen fell, too. They were both filled with the Spirit of God. (Alma 19:12-13)

When Ammon thanked the Lord for blessing the king and queen, he was also filled with the Spirit of God and fell to the ground.

Now all of King Lamoni's servants could see that the Lord was powerful, and they began to pray. The Spirit of God filled the king's servants, and they fell to the ground, also. **(Alma 19:14-16)**

Abish was a servant to the queen. She had faith in God and was excited when she saw what had happened. Abish knew that the king and his household were not dead. She knew that they had been filled with the Spirit of God and were gaining testimonies of the gospel. **(Alma 19:16-17)**

Abish ran from house to house telling the Lamanites the great things that had happened. She wanted the people come and see the power of God.

The people listened to Abish. They ran to King Lamoni's house to see what had happened. Some of the people did not understand. They thought that a great evil had come upon the king and his household for letting Ammon live in their land.

(Alma 19:17-21)

43

One of the Lamanite robbers saw Ammon laying on the ground. He was angry at Ammon for killing his brother. The robber tried to kill Ammon with his sword, but he was not able to kill Ammon. **(Alma 19:21-23)**

Instead, the Lamanite
robber fell dead to the
ground. The Lord would not
allow Ammon to be killed,
because He had promised to
protect Ammon from the
Lamanites. (Alma 19:22-23)

When the Lamanites saw that Ammon could not be killed, they began to argue about who Ammon really was.

Abish, the queen's servant, did not like to hear the people argue. She sadly walked to the queen and touched her hand.

Immediately, the queen arose. She praised God and thanked Him for the gospel. The queen took King Lamoni by the hand, and he arose, too.

King Lamoni was displeased when he heard his people arguing. He commanded the people to quit arguing, so he could teach them all the things that he had learned.

(Alma 19:24-31)

Ammon and the servants rose up too. They helped King Lamoni teach the gospel to the other Lamanites.

Many of the Lamanites were converted to the gospel. Ammon thanked the Lord for letting him share the gospel with the Lamanites.

(Alma 19:33-36)

"IN MY HEART"

From the Animated Video -

AMMON, MISSIONARY TO THE LAMANITES

IN MY HEART

Lyrics by
CAROL LYNN PEARSON

Music by
LEX DE AZEVEDO
Arr. by CINDY BONNELL BARNEY

THE FIRST ANIMATED VIDEO FROM 2 EXCITING VIDEO SERIES . . . .
PLUS COMPANION STORYBOOKS!

FAMILY ENTERTAINMENT NETWORK, INC. PRESENTS

Abraham and Isaac

ANIMATED STORIES FROM THE BIBLE

AWARD WINNER

THE ANIMATED STORIES FROM THE OLD TESTAMENT

Abraham and Isaac is the emotion-filled story of complete obedience and unreserved sacrifice. This beautifully animated story is the first of an exciting 12 tape video series which includes these best-loved stories from the Bible:

1. Abraham & Isaac
2. Joseph in Egypt
3. Samuel
4. Elijah
5. Daniel
6. Esther
*7. Moses
*8. Elisha
*9. Ruth
*10. David
*11. Solomon
*12. Nehemiah

THE ANIMATED HERO CLASSICS

LIVING HISTORY PRODUCTIONS, INC.

Christopher Columbus

ANIMATED HERO CLASSICS™
FULLY ANIMATED

AWARD WINNER

Sail along with Christopher Columbus to the new world through this thrilling animated video. **Christopher Columbus** is just the first animated story in this 12 tape series which includes such favorites as:

1. Christopher Columbus
2. William Bradford
3. General George Washington
4. Benjamin Franklin
5. Abraham Lincoln
6. Thomas Edison
*7. Florence Nightingale
*8. Pocahontas
*9. Louis Pasteur
*10. Alexander Bell
*11. Harriett Tubman
*12. Orville and Wilbur Wright

FULL COLOR COMPANION STORYBOOKS ARE ALSO AVAILABLE FOR EACH OF THESE EXCITING TITLES!

Children can follow along with their full color illustrated storybooks as they watch these inspiring videos again and again. These beautiful, hardbound storybooks will become bedtime favorites for children of all ages.

For further information, contact your Living Scriptures representative, local bookstore, or call toll-free 1-800-548-4647.

*Titles subject to change

Favorite stories from the New Testament come to life through these wonderful animated videos and companion storybooks.

Watch in awe as the greatest stories from the Bible are instilled in your children through the power of classical animation. The full color companion storybooks will become priceless treasures as they reinforce the values taught in each video story.

Your children and grandchildren will become better acquainted with the scriptures and the selfless love of the Master through these exciting productions.

Animated Stories from the New Testament include these 12 thrilling titles:

1. The King is Born
2. John the Baptist
3. The Prodigal Son
4. The Good Samaritan
5. The Miracles of Jesus
6. Saul of Tarsus
7. He is Risen
8. The Righteous Judge
9. Forgive Us Our Debts
10. The Kingdom of Heaven
11. Treasures in Heaven
12. The Ministry of Paul

For further information, contact your Living Scriptures representative, local bookstore, or call toll-free 1-800-548-4647.

THE ANIMATED STORIES FROM THE BOOK OF MORMON

Companion animated videos to enhance the value of your Book of Mormon Storybooks

These beautifully animated videos have thrilled thousands of families while teaching important, character-building ideals such as faith, obedience, honesty and many more. What better way to instill the principles of the gospel in your children.

Children will enjoy watching these outstanding videos again and again as they follow along with their illustrated storybooks.

The Animated Book of Mormon videos compliment each storybook and include the following faith-building stories from the Book of Mormon:

Nephi and the Brass Plates	The Brother of Jared	Helaman's Stripling Warriors
Journey to the Promised Land	The Joseph Smith Story	Alma and the Zoramites
Abinadi and King Noah	The Savior in America	The Tree of Life
The Conversion of Alma the Younger	Samuel and the Sign	Mormon and Moroni
Ammon, Missionary to the Lamanites		

For further information, contact your Living Scriptures representative, local bookstore, or call toll-free 1-800-548-4647.

FAVORITE SONGS FROM THE ANIMATED BOOK OF MORMON AND NEW TESTAMENT ON VIDEO AND AUDIO TAPES

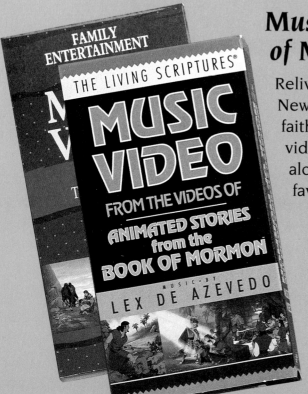

Music Videos from the Animated Book of Mormon and New Testament

Relive each animated story from the Book of Mormon and New Testament through these fantastic music videos. Each faith-building song, complete with animation from the videos in each series is included. Kids will love to sing along with the highlighted words as they watch their favorite parts from each video again and again.

Songs from the Animated Book of Mormon and New Testament on Audio Cassette Tape

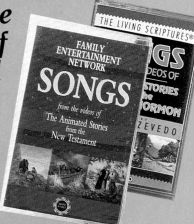

The heart-warming songs from the Animated Stories from the Book of Mormon and New Testament are available on separate audio cassette tapes. These beautiful tapes also include the full instrumental accompaniment, as well as the lyrics so families can sing along.

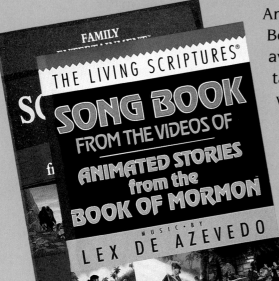

Song Books from the Animated Book of Mormon and New Testament

These beautiful musical arrangements are without equal for the best popular songs ever released on the Book of Mormon and New Testament. Each songbook also includes guitar chords for every song.

For further information, contact your Living Scriptures representative, local bookstore, or call toll-free 1-800-548-4647.